Snap it

love
ya   xoxo

SNAP IT!

ISBN: 978-1-956884-12-8

Contributing Editor: or all services completed
by Imprint Productions, Inc.
Cover Design: or all services completed
by Imprint Productions, Inc.

Printed in the United States of America
Published by Imprint Productions, Inc.
First Edition 2023

Contact:
info@imprintproductionsinc.com • www.imprintproductionsinc.com

FOREWORD

By Chesley McNeil-Chief Meteorologist/11Alive News

During the Coronavirus pandemic, the United States reported more than 1 million people had succumbed to the disease. You may likely have lost a loved one or friend. Takari Tatum lost both in one, Rudolph Tatum, his best friend and grandfather.

For a pre-teen that is a lot to deal with, but Ta'kari is a very unique and wise young man. You will appreciate how this inspiring young author developed a special way to deal with his loss and help others cope at the same time.

This is a very good book and reminds us that sometimes, even in our grief, we can do things that will change the world. Enjoy!

DEDICATION

This book is dedicated in loving memory of Rudolph Roeshell Tatum and Charlissia Gates for being encouragers and always shining a light on me so I can be my best. You have inspired me on my mental health journey. You have taught me that mental health matters and that I can overcome stress and anxiety. I love you, my Heavenly Family. Gone, but never forgotten.

ACKNOWLEDGMENTS

I'd like to acknowledge Mrs. Laurie Mendenhall from Varner Elementary school in Powder Springs, Georgia, for assigning me an awesome community service project. Without that project, this book wouldn't be possible. Also, a big thank you to Mrs. Robin Glover, my former art teacher and the sketch artist of this book. During my time at Varner Elementary School in Powder Springs, Georgia, Mrs. Glover taught me that drawing was relaxing and rewarding. Drawing is a passion of mine that wouldn't exist if she wasn't in my life. Without her guidance with this book, it wouldn't exist. Thank you to Ms. Althea Singletary and the rest of the Varner administrative staff for their support.

Also, I'd like to acknowledge Ms. Bonnie Hannah, Ms. Sarah Galyean, Ms. Kim Jones, Ms. Miriam Goodfriend, and the rest of the NAMI team that I've encountered. Because of this one video they saw on my Facebook account, they decided to help me on my great, unending, mental health journey.

Next, I'd love to acknowledge my loving family. First of all, Ms. Gwendolyn Tatum, my grandmother, and Co-Author who raised me from the moment I was born. Reflecting on all our memories of us is tear-jerking. We are a dynamic duo. We always work as a team. I also acknowledge Mr. Trevor Tatum, my dad, who loved me through every second of my life. His support means the world to me. He always keeps a smile on my face encouraging me to try new things. Mr. Theodore Tatum the "Tech Guru" of our club. He always has a solution to our problems while also keeping his humorous nature and funny smile. Mr. Terrell Tatum always keeps our household sane with his knowledge and jokes. No matter the circumstance, he can and will make everyone burst out in laughter. That was so needed. Ms. Evangeline Stanford, my rubber band "Expert Maker" who easily learned to make the bracelets, it's been an everlasting hobby. Even though she's cities away, she can still swiftly make rubber band bracelets. At first, I underestimated how many she could make in a week, but after the bands came in the mail, my face lit up with joy.

Also, I'd like to thank the rest of my family including my mom, Ms. Briannia Powell, my grandmother, Mrs. Sherry McCraken, and friends for reviewing my work so I can be the best person and author that I can be. Finally, I would like to thank my publisher, Dr. Brunetta Nelson, and all members of Imprint Productions, Inc.

ABOUT THE AUTHOR

Ta'kari had a school project. He is a very intuitive child, and he noticed that Covid-19 had taken a toll on his friends and family. He felt the stress and anxiety all around him. So, he decided to focus his project on mental health. He designed stress bracelets. When someone wears the bracelet, they acknowledge that mental health is real. Snapping the bracelet against your wrist, breathing and relaxing can make you feel better. Because of her mental health struggles, Ta'kari's grandmother, Gwen, supported and embraced this idea. They decided to go around the country spreading the word that mental health is not a stigma, but something to acknowledge, embrace and overcome.

They decided to write a children's book and explain their mental health journey. This is how **Snap It** was born. Ta'kari and his grandmother wanted to share that people can survive mental health challenges and become stronger from it. They hope everyone enjoys the book and if they are struggling with mental health issues to seek help and help spread the word that mental illness is not something to be ashamed of. So, remember when you feel stressed or anxious, just **Snap It** and breathe.

The weather outside was gray and gloomy. This was how I felt inside. My family was crying and mourning (voc) the loss of my grandpa. I was getting ready to go to Grandpa's funeral. Everyone was dressed in my grandpa's favorite colors which were purple, black, and blue. I knew this day was coming, but how do I say goodbye to not just my grandpa, but my best friend?

I remember when Grandpa got sick. He would just lay in bed. He wouldn't eat. He couldn't walk; he would just lay there with his eyes closed. It made me so sad. I would go to school broken-hearted (voc) and come home heartbroken. (voc)

Suddenly, I didn't feel like eating or sleeping either.

The days after the funeral were stressful for me. As I was sitting in school with my classmates, this boy Kevin asked," Why are you lookin' so sad? Are you gonna cry or somethin'? You big baby."

I responded, "Hey man go on somewhere with that, I ain't no baby." Kevin said, "Okay man, take it easy." That made me angry and I responded, "I'll give you okay," and I punched Kevin straight in the nose. The teacher came running, and I knew I was in trouble.

Mrs. Mendenhall called my Grandma and said, "Hello, Mrs. Tatum. Do you have a minute? Well, we need to talk about Ta'kari. I am very concerned. He hasn't been paying attention in class, he hasn't been prepared for class, he failed his last math test, and today he punched a student. I have seen changes in his personality and behavior." "Oh dear," said grandma. "He has not taken the death of his grandpa well. I have noticed some behavior changes as well. Let me talk with his dad to come up with a solution to help him."

When I got home from school, I didn't have the words to express what I was feeling. I just knew I had a lump in my throat that felt like I had swallowed a jawbreaker. My stomach felt like I devoured a bag of jolly ranchers. "Grandma, I don't feel well. Everything hurts."

"I'm sorry, honey. Why don't you go and lay down before dinner?" said Grandma.

This advice didn't help at all. I just kept remembering all the good times with Grandpa. Just lying there made me dizzy and dazed, and I started to cry.

Grandpa was a gamer. He taught me how to play chess when I was just 5 years old. We could play for hours. I know he would let me win, sometimes. We loved to share ice cream; it was fun making sundaes with him. I loved the whipped cream, and he loved the sprinkles.

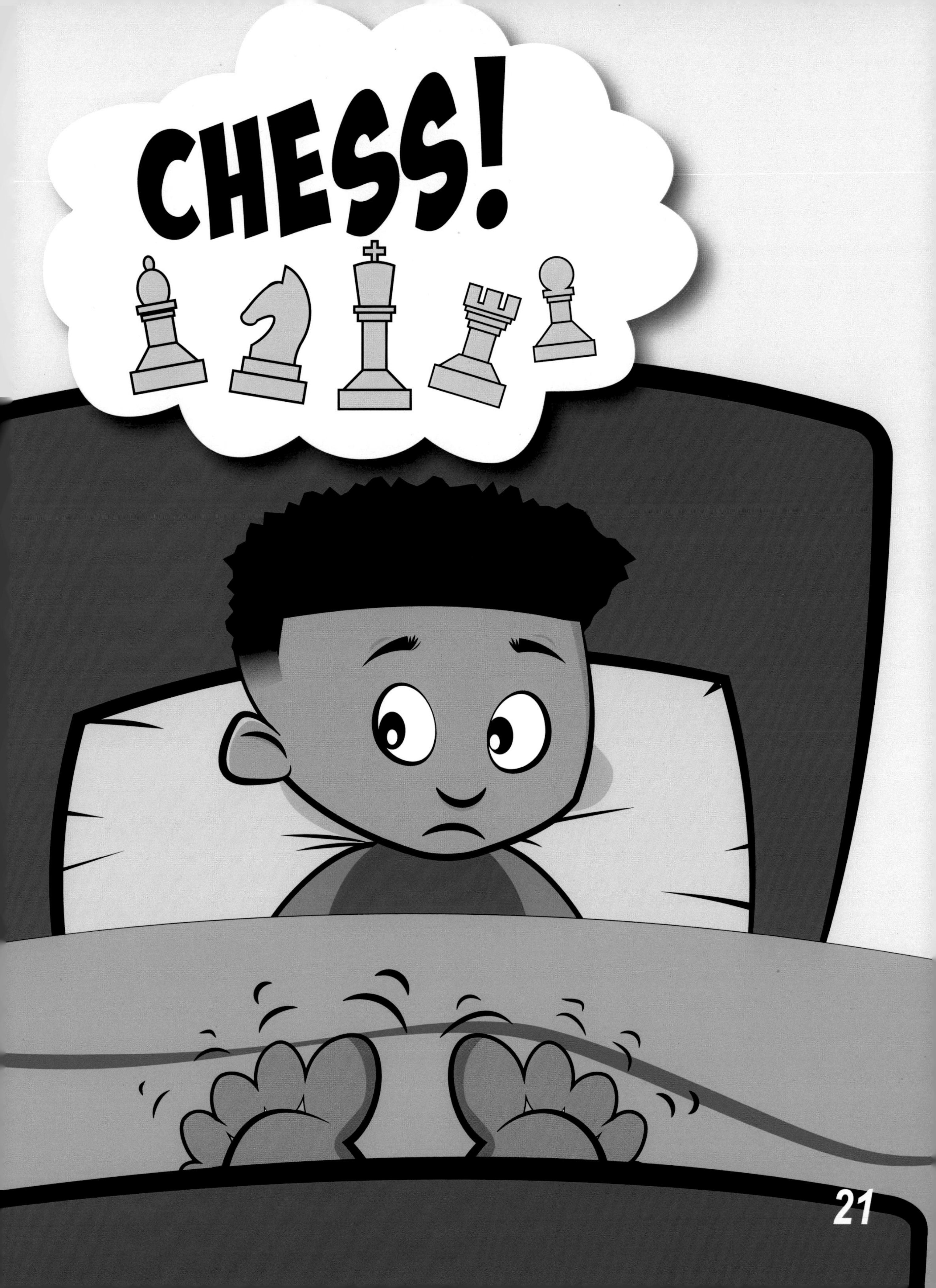
CHESS!

When I won my first baseball tournament, he was there. He took all the pictures and held the plaque for me. Oh, he was so proud. We would always go to different states. I remember going to Florida and seeing a giant alligator. It was an amazing time I spent with him on that trip. When we went to the beach, I loved burying him in the sand. We would always have a good time together.

I heard my dad come in. "Hi, I'm sorry I'm late," dad shouts to my grandma. "I was at a business meeting all day, and I just got your message. What's going on with buddy?" "I got a call from his teacher, grandma replied. "He hit a student and he's not doing well in school. He's in his room right now, saying he isn't feeling well, and I told him to lay down."

"What's up Buddy? Are you ok?" asked Dad.

"No Dad, I'm not," I answered. "I keep thinking about Grandpa, and it makes me very sad. I don't know what to do."
"It's okay to remember the good times with Grandpa and be sad about it," he said. I feel sad sometimes too. I guess I forgot that kids grieve (voc) just like adults. You have never experienced a loss like this before and you don't know how to handle it. I remember hearing about how feeling the sting of a rubber band next to your skin can relieve stress (voc) and de-pression. (voc) Here, take this rubber band bracelet I got at a meeting at work to-day. You are supposed to wear it if you feel weak or anxious. (voc)You snap it against your wrist and breathe. Do you want to try it now?" said Dad.

"I don't know Dad." I answered. "Nothing seems to work. I don't see how a little, simple rubber band can make a difference." "Well, it may work or it may not, but it wouldn't hurt to try. Would it?" said dad. "Sure dad," I said.

I immediately slipped the bracelet on my wrist. The bracelet was in my grandpa's favorite colors. This made me smile. I stretched the bracelet on my wrist and Snapped It. I felt the sting, and I took a deep breath and breathed out. I immediately felt a sense of relief and tension leaving my body. "It really worked," I sighed aloud.

After a good night's sleep, I found my parents in the kitchen. "I feel so much better this morning. I am going to try to do better in school, and I am going to apologize to Kevin and my teacher."

"That's great, honey," grandma responded. "Do you think the bracelet helped?", Dad asked.

"Yes", I replied. "I'm going to wear it all day to remind me to stay calm and breathe when I feel anger or stress."

"Grandpa and I are so proud of you!" shouted Dad. This made me smile.

"Now, I smell bacon. Grandma, can I get a plate?"

33

THE END

VOCABULARY

1. **Anxious:** ˈaŋ(k)-shəs
Synonyms of anxious
1: characterized by extreme uneasiness of mind or brooding fear about some contingency : WORRIED. Anxious parents
2: characterized by, resulting from, or causing anxiety : WORRYING
They spent an anxious night.
3: ardently or earnestly wishing. *She was anxious to learn more.*
anxiously adverb, anxiousness noun

2. **Broken-Hearted**: ˈbrō-kən-ˈhär-təd
Synonyms of brokenhearted
1: overcome by grief or despair

3. **Depression**: di-ˈpre-shən
Plural depressions
Synonyms of depression
1: an act of depressing or a state of being depressed: such as
 a state of feeling sad : low spirits : MELANCHOLY
specifically : a mood disorder that is marked by varying degrees of sadness, despair, and loneliness and that is typically accompanied by inactivity, guilt, loss of concentration, social withdrawal, sleep disturbances, and sometimes suicidal tendencies see also CLINICAL DEPRESSION, MAJOR DEPRESSION, POSTPARTUM DEPRESSION

4. **Grieve**: ˈgrēv
grieved; grieving
Synonyms of grieve
transitive verb
1: to cause to suffer : DISTRESS
it grieves me to see him this way
2: to feel or show grief over
grieving the death of her son
3: to submit a formal grievance concerning

35

5. **Heartbroken**: ˈhärt-ˌbrō-kən
Synonyms of heartbroken
overcome by sorrow

6. **Mourning**: ˈmȯr-niŋ
Synonyms of mourning
1: the act of sorrowing
She is still in mourning for her dead husband.
2a: an outward sign (such as black clothes or an armband) of grief for
a person's death
b: a period of time during which signs of grief are shown
After a long mourning, they resumed their ordinary dress.

7. **Stress**: ˈstres
Synonyms of stress
a state resulting from a stress
especially : one of bodily or mental tension resulting from factors
that tend to alter an existent equilibrium
job-related stress